BEATLES BIG NOTE

Order No. NO 17428 ISBN: 0-86001-039-2
Exclusive distributors:
Music Sales Limited, 78 Newman Street, London W1P 3LA.
Music Sales Australia, 27 Clarendon Street, Artarmon, Sydney, Australia 2064.

WISE PUBLICATIONS
London/New York/Sydney

Across The Universe

Words and Music by
JOHN LENNON and
PAUL McCARTNEY

All My Loving

Words and Music by
JOHN LENNON and
PAUL McCARTNEY

All Together Now

Words and Music by
JOHN LENNON and
PAUL McCARTNEY

All You Need Is Love

Words and Music by
JOHN LENNON and
PAUL McCARTNEY

And I Love Her

Words and Music by
JOHN LENNON and
PAUL McCARTNEY

Slowly, with expression

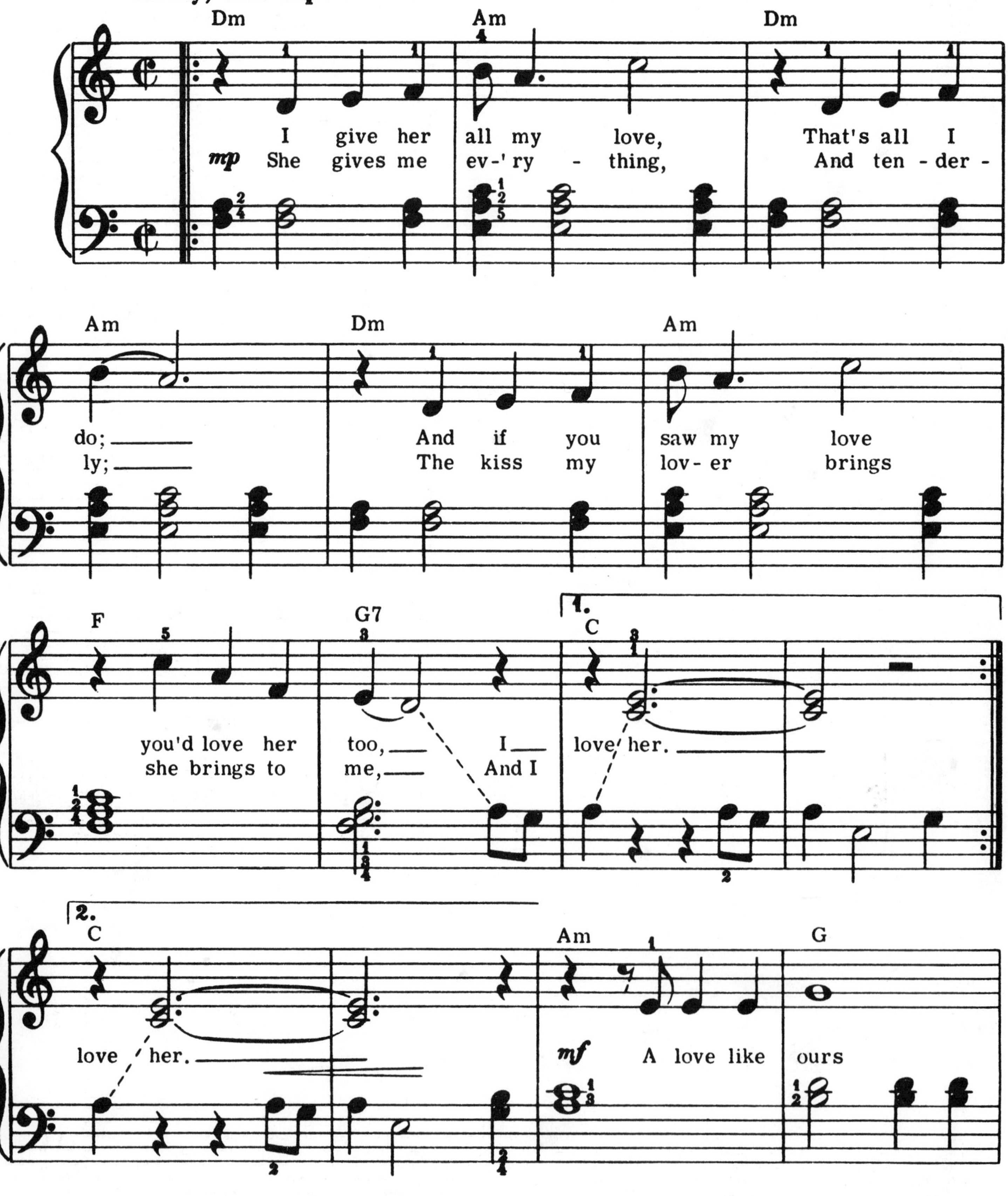

Dm Am Dm
I give her all my love, That's all I
mp She gives me ev-'ry - thing, And ten - der -
Am Dm Am
do; And if you saw my love
ly; The kiss my lov - er brings
F G7 1. C
you'd love her too, I love her.
she brings to me, And I
2. C Am G
love her. mf A love like ours

Can't Buy Me Love

Words and Music by
JOHN LENNON and
PAUL McCARTNEY

Carry That Weight

Words and Music by
JOHN LENNON and
PAUL McCARTNEY

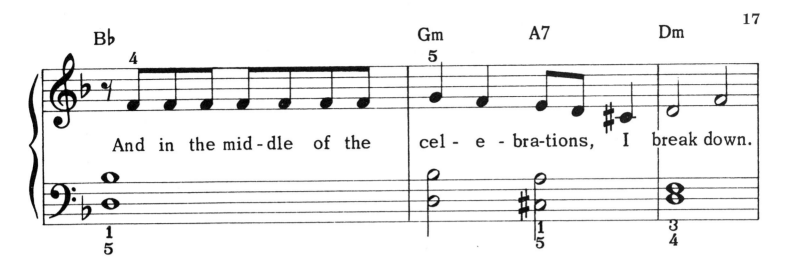

Come Together

Words and Music by
JOHN LENNON and
PAUL McCARTNEY

Slow beat

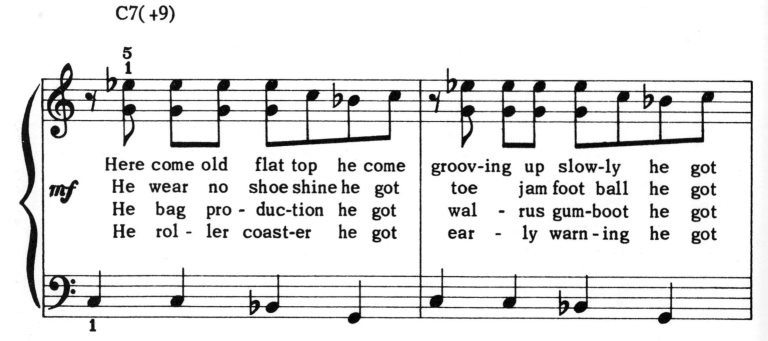

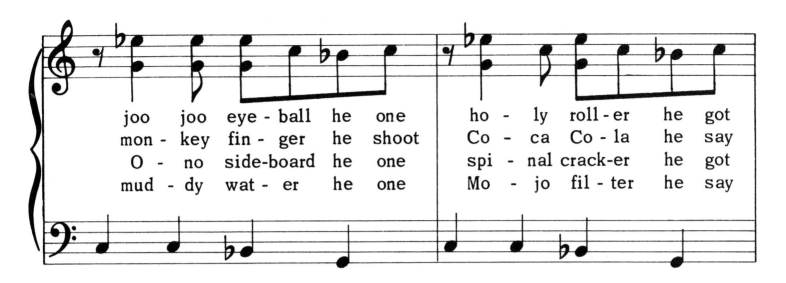

joo joo eye - ball he one   ho - ly roll - er he got
mon - key fin - ger he shoot   Co - ca Co - la he say
O - no side-board he one   spi - nal crack-er he got
mud - dy wat - er he one   Mo - jo fil - ter he say

hair down   to his knee.
I know you   you know me.
feet down be - low his knee.
one and one and one is three.

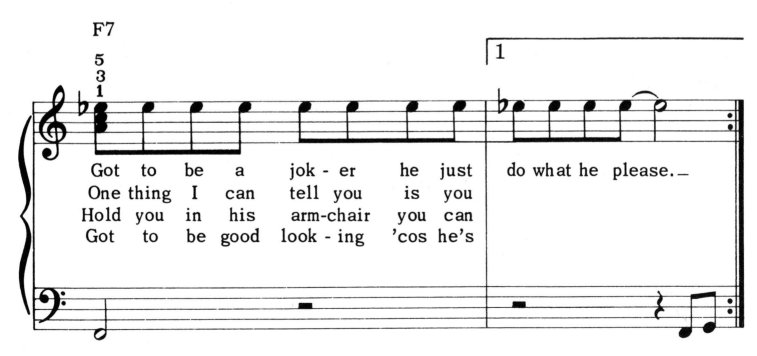

Got to be a jok - er he just   do what he please.
One thing I can tell you is you
Hold you in his arm-chair you can
Got to be good look - ing 'cos he's

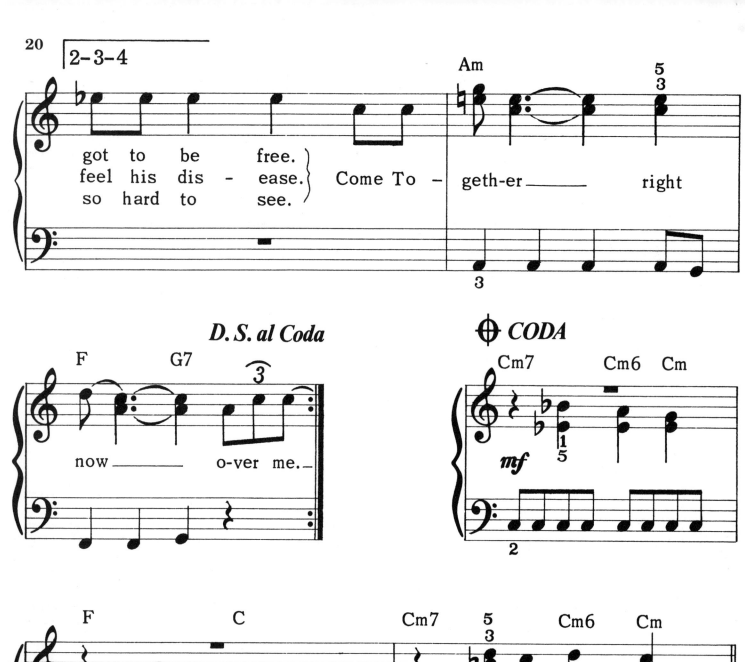

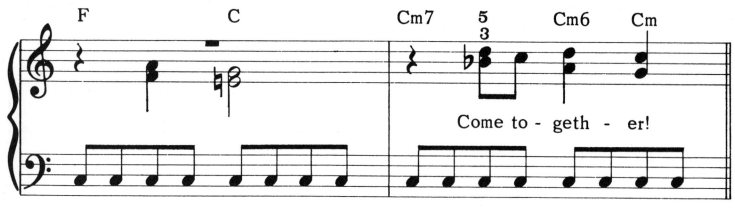

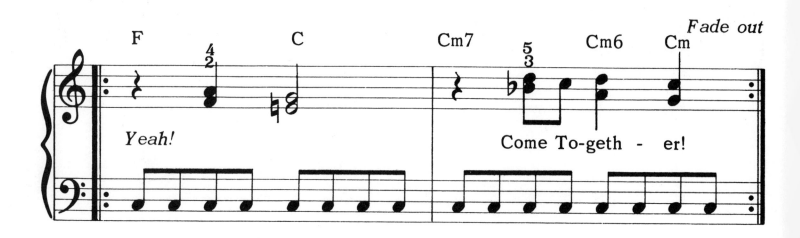

Give Peace A Chance

Words and Music by
JOHN LENNON and
PAUL McCARTNEY

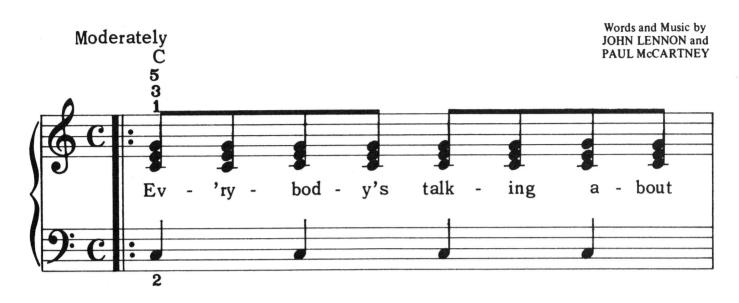

Ev - 'ry - bod - y's talk - ing a - bout

Bag - is - m, Shag - is - m, Drag - is - m, Mad - is - m,
Min - is - ters, Sin - is - ters, Ban - is - ters, and Can - is - ters,
Rev- o - lu - tion, Ev- o - lu - tion, Mas - ti - ca - tion, Fla - gel - la - tion,
John and Yo - ko, Tim - my Lea - ry, Rose - ma - ry, Tom - my Smoth - ers

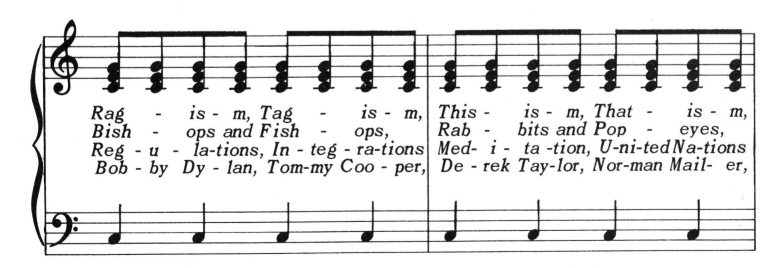

Rag - is - m, Tag - is - m, This - is - m, That - is - m,
Bish - ops and Fish - ops, Rab - bits and Pop - eyes,
Reg - u - la - tions, In - teg - ra - tions Med - i - ta - tion, U - ni - ted Na - tions
Bob - by Dy - lan, Tom - my Coo - per, De - rek Tay - lor, Nor - man Mail - er,

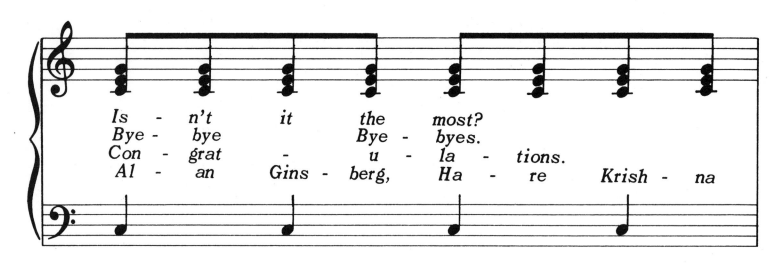

Is - n't it the most?
Bye - bye Bye - byes.
Con - grat - u - la - tions.
Al - an Gins - berg, Ha - re Krish - na

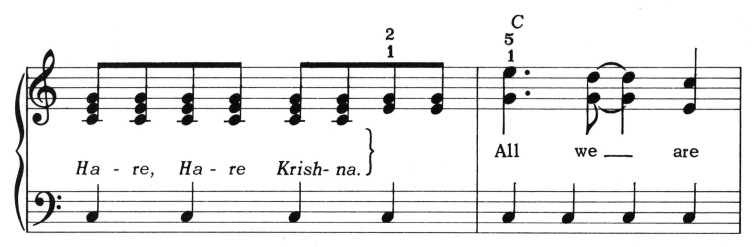

Ha - re, Ha - re Krish- na.

C

All we ___ are

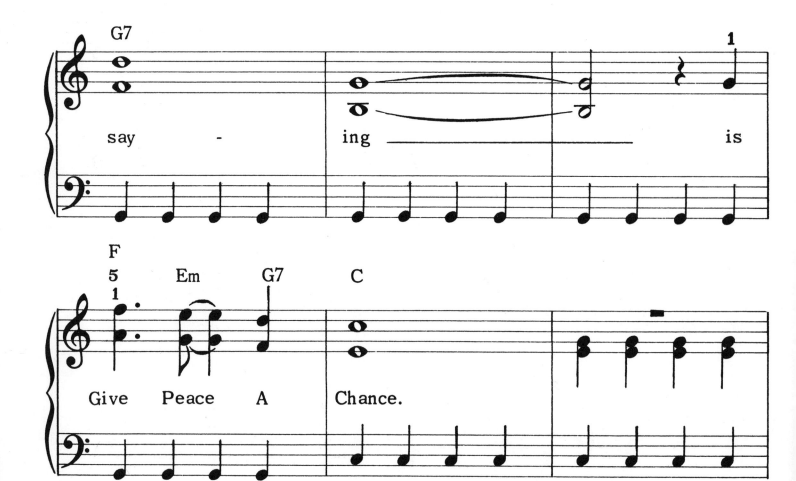

G7

say - ing _____ is

F   Em   G7   C

Give Peace A   Chance.

Day Tripper

Words and Music by
JOHN LENNON and
PAUL McCARTNEY

Eight Days A Week

Words and Music by
JOHN LENNON and
PAUL McCARTNEY

Eleanor Rigby

Words and Music by
JOHN LENNON and
PAUL McCARTNEY

Moderately, with a steady beat

1. E - lea - nor Rig - by, picks up the rice ___ in a
2. Fa - ther Mc Ken - zie writ - ing the words ___ of a
3. E - lea - nor Rig - by, died in the church ___ and was

church where a wed-ding has been ___ lives in a dream. ___
ser - mon that no one will hear, ___ no one comes near. ___
bur - ried a - long with her name, ___ no-bod-y came. ___

Waits at the win - dow, wear - ing the face ___ that she
Look at him work - ing, darn - ing the socks ___ in the
Fa - ther Mc Ken - zie, wip - ing the dirt ___ from his

Get Back

Words and Music by
JOHN LENNON and
PAUL McCARTNEY

Got To Get You Into My Life

Words and Music by
JOHN LENNON and
PAUL McCARTNEY

You didn't run, you didn't lie
You knew I wanted just to hold you.
And had you gone you knew in time
We'd meet again for I'd have told you.
Ooh, you were meant to be near me.
Ooh, and I want you to hear me
Say we'll be together ev'ry day.
Got to get you into my life!

What can I do, what can I be,
When I'm with you I want to stay there.
If I'm true I'll never leave
And if I do I know the way there.
Ooh, then I suddenly see you.
Ooh, did I tell you I need you
Ev'ry single day of my life?
Got to get you into my life!

A Hard Day's Night

Words and Music by
JOHN LENNON and
PAUL McCARTNEY

Hello, Goodbye

Words and Music by
JOHN LENNON and
PAUL McCARTNEY

Help!

Words and Music by
JOHN LENNON and
PAUL McCARTNEY

Hey Jude

Words and Music by
JOHN LENNON and
PAUL McCARTNEY

Here, There And Everywhere

Words and Music by
JOHN LENNON and
PAUL McCARTNEY

In My Life

Words and Music by
JOHN LENNON and
PAUL McCARTNEY

Moderately

There are plac-es I'll re-mem-ber All my life,___ though some have changed Some for-ev-er, not for bet-ter, Some have gone___ and some re-main. All these plac-es_ had_ their_ mo-ments With lov-ers and friends I still can re-call. Some are

But of all these friends and lovers,
There is no one compares with you
And these mem'ries lose their meaning
When I think of love as something new.
Though I know I'll never lose affection
For people and things that went before,
I know I'll often stop and think about them,
In my life I'll love you more.

I've Got A Feeling

Words and Music by
JOHN LENNON and
PAUL McCARTNEY

Moderately Slow

D.S. al Coda

some-bod-y who looked like you.

Oh please believe me
I'd hate to miss the train
Oh yeah, oh yeah.
And if you leave me
I won't be late again,
Oh no, oh no, oh no.
Yeah, yeah, I've got a feeling, yeah!

I've got a feeling
That keeps me on my toes,
Oh yeah, oh yeah.
I've got a feeling
I think that ev'rybody knows,
Oh yeah, oh yeah, oh yeah.
Yeah, Yeah, I've got a feeling, yeah!

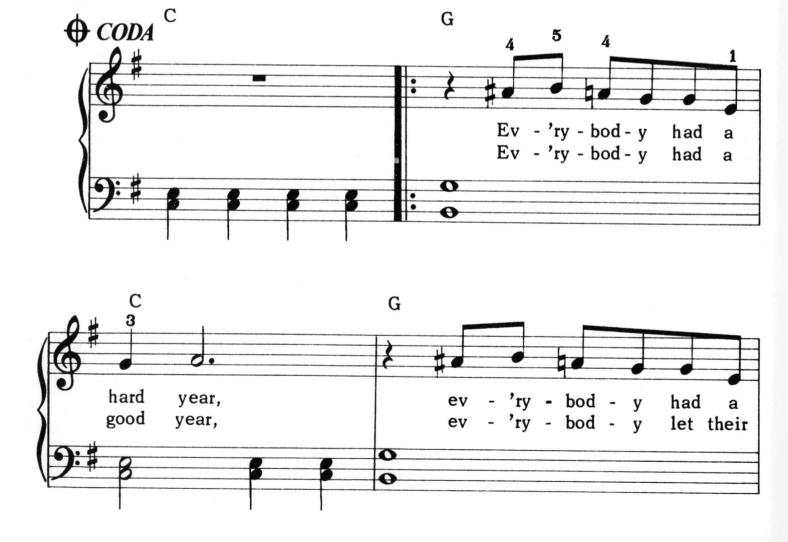

Ev - 'ry - bod - y had a
Ev - 'ry - bod - y had a

hard   year,
good   year,

ev - 'ry - bod - y had a
ev - 'ry - bod - y let their

Lady Madonna

Words and Music by
JOHN LENNON and
PAUL McCARTNEY

Brightly, with a beat

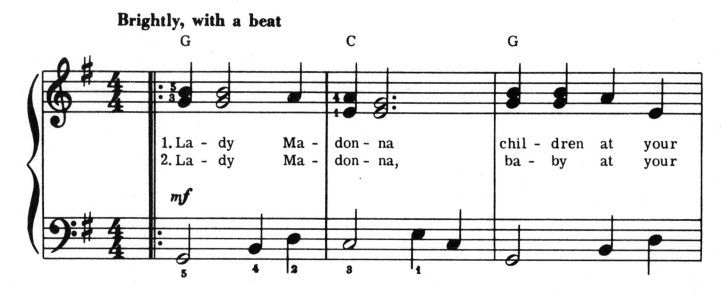

Let It Be

Words and Music by
JOHN LENNON and
PAUL McCARTNEY

The Long and Winding Road

Words and Music by
JOHN LENNON and
PAUL McCARTNEY

Slowly

Michelle

Words and Music by
JOHN LENNON and
PAUL McCARTNEY

Norwegian Wood
(This Bird Has Flown)

Words and Music by
JOHN LENNON and
PAUL McCARTNEY

She asked me to stay and she told me to sit an-y-where.

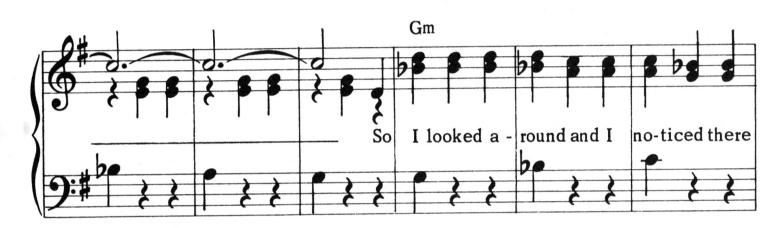

So I looked a-round and I no-ticed there

2nd time D.C. al Fine

was-n't a chair.

I sat on a rug, biding my time,
drinking her wine;
We talked until two, and then she said,
"It's time for bed."

She told me she worked in the morning
and started to laugh.
I told her I didn't and crawled off to
sleep in the bath.

And when I awoke, I was alone,
this bird had flown;
So I lit a fire, isn't it good,
Norwegian Wood?

Nowhere Man

Words and Music by
JOHN LENNON and
PAUL McCARTNEY

Paperback Writer

Words and Music by
JOHN LENNON and
PAUL McCARTNEY

Dail - y Mail; It's a stead - y job, but he

wants to be a pa - per back writ - er,

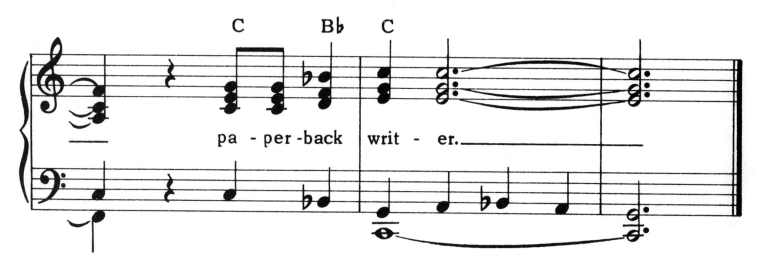

pa - per -back writ - er.

It's a thousand pages, give or take a few,
I'll be writing more in a week or two.
I can make it longer if you like the style,
I can change it 'round and I want to be a paperback writer,
    paperback writer.

If you really like it you can have the rights,
It could make a million for you overnight.
If you must return it you can send it here;
But I need a break and I want to be a paperback writer,
    paperback writer.

Penny Lane

Words and Music by
JOHN LENNON and
PAUL McCARTNEY

Moderately

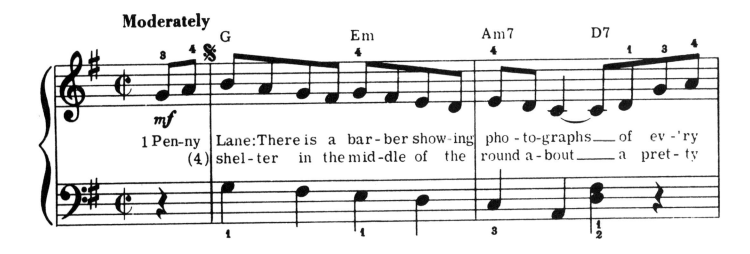

1 Pen-ny Lane: There is a bar-ber show-ing pho-to-graphs___ of ev-'ry
(4) shel-ter in the mid-dle of the round a-bout___ a pret-ty

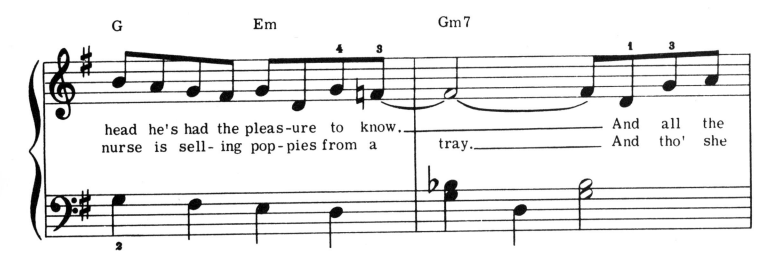

head he's had the pleas-ure to know.___ And all the
nurse is sell-ing pop-pies from a tray.___ And tho' she

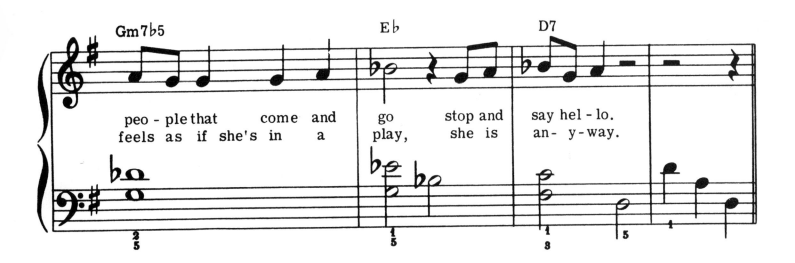

peo-ple that come and go, stop and say hel-lo.
feels as if she's in a play, she is an-y-way.

73

Sgt. Pepper's Lonely Hearts Club Band

Words and Music by
JOHN LENNON and
PAUL McCARTNEY

She Came In
Through The Bathroom Window

Words and Music by
JOHN LENNON and
PAUL McCARTNEY

Moderately Slow

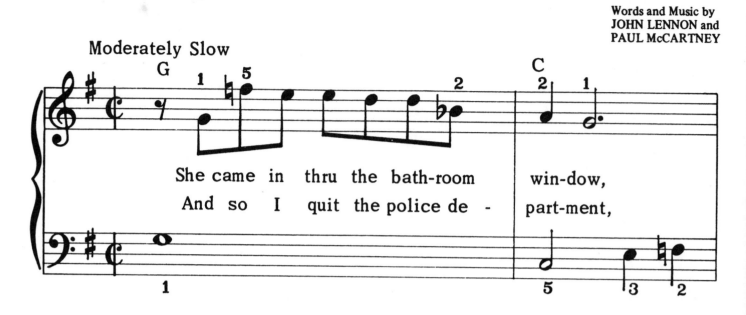

She came in thru the bath-room win-dow,
And so I quit the police de - part-ment,

Pro - tect - ed by a sil - ver spoon.____
And got my - self a stead - y job.____

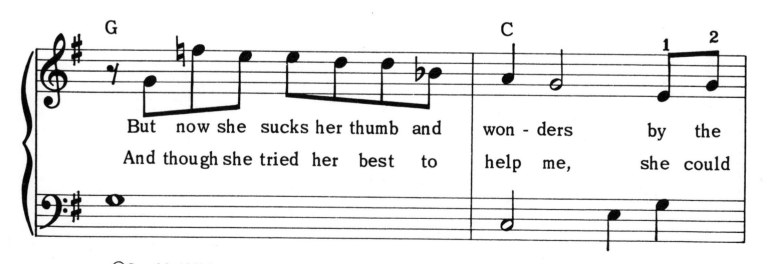

But now she sucks her thumb and won - ders by the
And though she tried her best to help me, she could

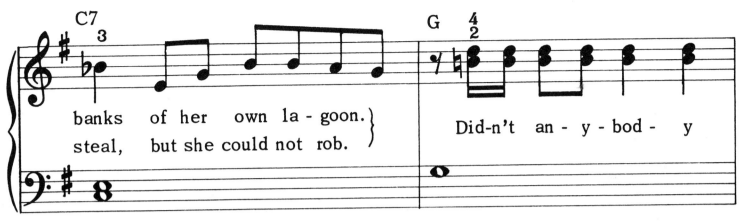

banks   of her   own la - goon.
steal,   but she could not rob.

Did-n't an - y - bod - y

tell   her?

Did-n't an - y - bod - y

see?

Sun - day's on   the   phone   to

Mon - day,

Tues-day's on the   phone   to

me.

She said she'd al - ways been a

dan - cer,

She worked at fif - teen clubs a

day. _____

And though she thought I knew the

an - swer, Well, I knew what I could not say. _____

Strawberry Fields Forever

Words and Music by
JOHN LENNON and
PAUL McCARTNEY

Let me take you down 'cause I'm goin' to Strawberry Fields.
Nothing is real, and nothing to get hung about,
Strawberry Fields forever.
No one I think is in my tree,
I mean it just might be high or low.
That is you know you can't tune in but it's all right.
That is, I think it's not too bad.

Let me take you down 'cause I'm goin' to Strawberry Fields.
Nothing is real, and nothing to get hung about,
Strawberry Fields forever.
Always know, sometimes think it's me.
But you know and I know it's a dream.
I think I know of thee, ah yes, but it's all wrong.
That is, I think I disagree.

Ticket To Ride

Words and Music by
JOHN LENNON and
PAUL McCARTNEY

With A Little Help From My Friends

Words and Music by
JOHN LENNON and
PAUL McCARTNEY

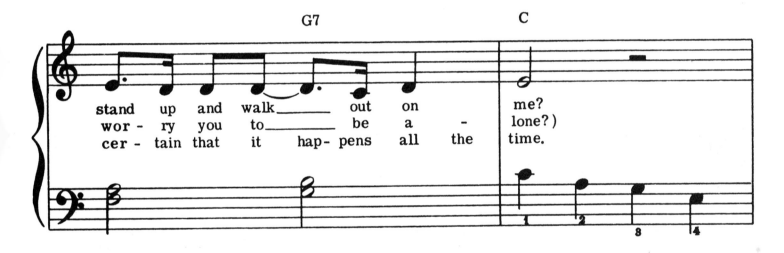

We Can Work It Out

Think of what you're saying
You can get it wrong and still you think that it's all right.
Think of what I'm saying,
We can work it out and get it straight or say good—night.
We can work it out,
We can work it out.

Try to see it my way,
Only time will tell if I am right or I am wrong.
While you see it your way,
There's a chance that we might fall apart before too long.
We can work it out,
We can work it out.

Yellow Submarine

Words and Music by
JOHN LENNON and
PAUL McCARTNEY

Yesterday

Words and Music by
JOHN LENNON and
PAUL McCARTNEY

World Without Love

Words and Music by
JOHN LENNON and
PAUL McCARTNEY

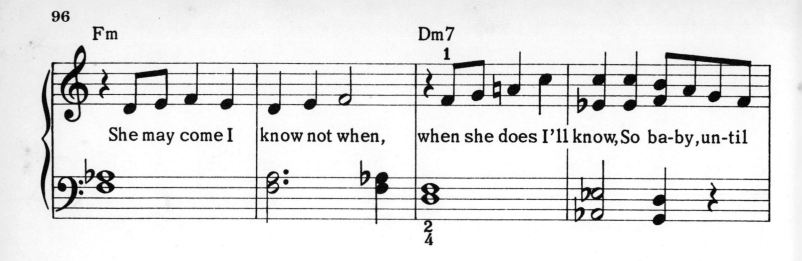

Reproduced and printed by
Halstan & Co. Ltd., Amersham, Bucks., England